Dr. Seuss'
THE **CAT IN THE HAT**

Based on the Movie

SALLY

MOM

CONRAD

FISH

THE CAT

LAWRENCE QUINN

NEVINS

MRS. KWAN

THINGS

BACKGROUND ON OFF MUSIC

STOP

1

In a house on a street **not unlike** any other, live Sally and Conrad, a sister and brother.

TO DO LIST

aren't
can't
didn't
doesn't
hasn't
don't
I'll

isn't
shan't
shouldn't
wasn't
won't
wouldn't
you're

Contraction: Two words combined to make one word.

"Tonight is my party,
so don't make a mess.
Don't make **cupcakes**," said Mom,
"and do not touch my dress!"

CONTRACTION GAME

repeat

STOP

3

They **slumped** in their chairs, much too sad to **complain**. They felt **gloomy** and **glum** and it started to rain.

They **heard** **hear** a loud BUMP

and they **jump** **jumped** from their chairs.

Yes, they **jump** **jumped** from the BUMP

that they **heard** **hear** from upstairs.

They **ran** **run** to the closet

and **opened** **open** the door.

They **look** **looked** this way and that,

but they **knew** **know** not what for.

And then what they **see** **saw**

makes **made** them stop

just like that. Yes, they **stopped** **stop**

and they **stare** **stared**

at The Cat in the Hat!

The Cat **tipped his hat** and he made a low bow. "Are you ready to smile? Showtime is right now!"

quick   carefully   stinky

quickly   clever   loudly

hilarious   slowly   brilliant

quietly   scary   wildly

hairy   strangely   slimy

ADJ. ADV.

"SEE HERE!" **cried** the fish.
"You will turn my scales gray.
Do not play with this cat
while your **mother's** away!"

microwave

cat

refrigerator

fish

teapot

dog

Conrad

Sally

They jumped on the couch.
The Cat hung from the **ceiling**.
They messed up the room,
and it was a fun feeling!

"Now **let's** go make cupcakes. We'll clean this mess later. You can have lots of fun with the **cupcake-inator**!"

horseradish

cupcake-inator

marshmallow

hairball

pepper

SOAP

soap

CHOCO

chocolate

ketchup

macaroni

mayonnaise

babysitter

PRACTICE

SYLLABLE GAME

repeat

STOP

9

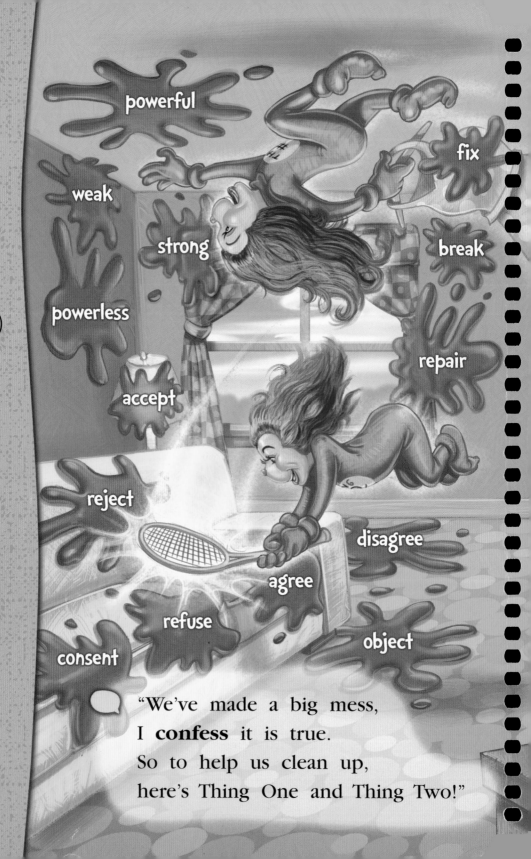

"We've made a big mess,
I **confess** it is true.
So to help us clean up,
here's Thing One and Thing Two!"

"**Please** keep this **crate** closed,"
The Cat **cautioned politely**.
And just to make certain,
he locked it up tightly.

GOTCHA!

"The crate's been unlocked!"
said The Cat with a holler,
"and Nevins has got the lock
stuck on his collar!"

They chased after Nevins.
They raced into town.
It's a lucky thing **S.L.O.W**.
doesn't ever slow down!

Quinn chased after them,
so they hid in a club.
There was music and dancing
and lots of **hubbub**.

They pushed through the dancers
who **crowded** the floor.
Then they rushed up the stairs,
and they ran out the door.

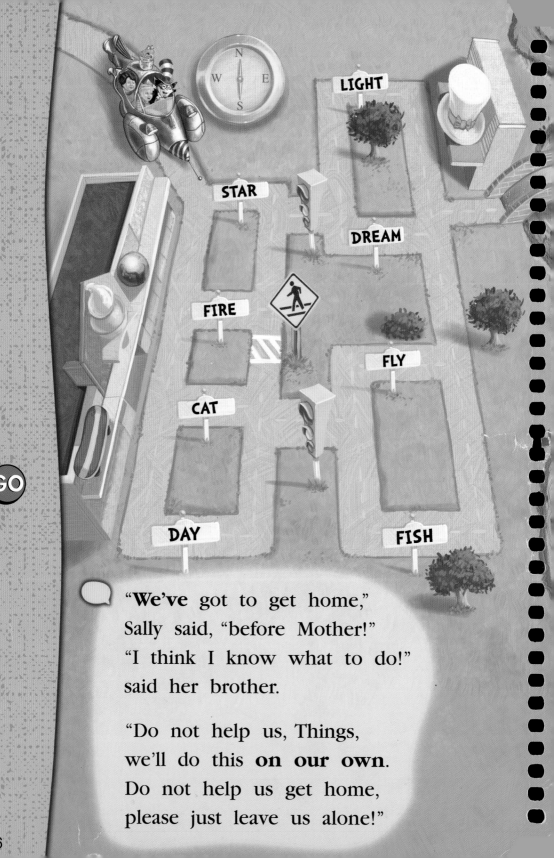

"**We've** got to get home,"
Sally said, "before Mother!"
"I think I know what to do!"
said her brother.

"Do not help us, Things,
we'll do this **on our own**.
Do not help us get home,
please just leave us alone!"

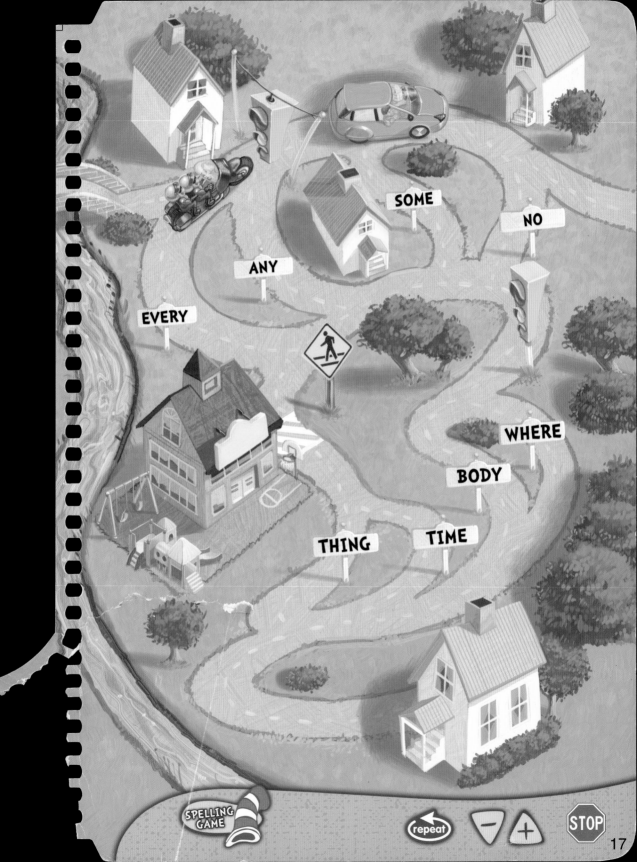

CONRAD SALLY THE CAT

WILL

MUST CAN THE FISH

TICKLE

SPIN

GO

They quickly were home and were **nearly** too late. Using **teamwork** they put the lid back on the crate.

SCARE

HUG

THE HOUSE

THIS MESS

A CUPCAKE

THE CRATE

"I won't help you clean.
You must **suffer your fate**.
Conrad broke my one rule
when he opened the crate."

"GET OUT!" the kids told him.
"We've got work to do.
This whole house is a mess,
and it's all thanks to you!"

GO

So The Cat left the house
with his face to the **weather**.
"Mom will be mad,
but we'll face it together."

Then came a surprise,
and a big one at that!
For just who had **returned**,
but The Cat in the Hat!

He rode in on D.I.R.T.,
his **fantastic** machine.
In a matter of moments,
the house was all clean.

ay

ee

coat

tray

ea

peel

steam

mail

leash

PRACTICE

SPELLING GAME

repeat − +

STOP

23

"I'm home, kids!" Mom called.
"Come and tell me what's new."
Conrad tried not to smile,
and Sally did, too.

Keep your child learning by leaps and bounds with

Leap's Pond™

Activity and Game Books

Subscribe to the Leap's Pond series! Each fun-filled, activity-packed book will be delivered right to your door!

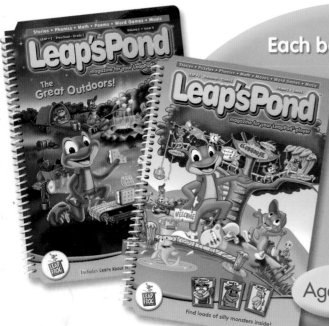

Each book teaches:

- Language Arts
- Math
- Social Sciences
- Music
- Science
- Foreign Language
- And Much More!

Ages 4-7

" *Leap's Pond makes my son feel special. He loves getting his own mail! It has helped him get ready for school and he doesn't even realize it's educational!* "

Rosie, Mother of a 5-year-old

Sign up at
www.leapfrog.com/leapspond
and get hours of learning fun
delivered to your door.

Not available in all markets.